KAHALA

KAHALA

Where the Rainbow Ends

By Guy and Pam Buffet
Illustrated by Guy Buffet
Edited by Ruth Tabrah

 An Island Heritage Book

Second Printing 1979
Copyright © 1973
Island Heritage Limited
ALL RIGHTS RESERVED
Library of Congress
Catalog Number 72-76459
ISBN Trade 0-8348-3021-3
Printed and bound in Hong Kong

Island Heritage Limited
828 Fort Street Mall
Suite 400
Honolulu, Hawaii 96813
Phone: (808) 524-7400

Island Heritage Limited is a
subsidiary of Honolulu Publishing Company, Ltd.

 An Island Heritage Book

To Jean and Zohmah Charlot

In Manoa, valley of the rainbows, there once was born a child of rare beauty. She was named Kahala-o-Puna for the tree that bears the flower of love.

She lived surrounded by birds and animals and was always happy. To see her smile made the people of Manoa feel they had been given a gift of joy.

Pueo, the blonde owl of Hawaii was her aumakua, her guardian. If she were ever in trouble, Kahala knew the great owl would come to her aid.

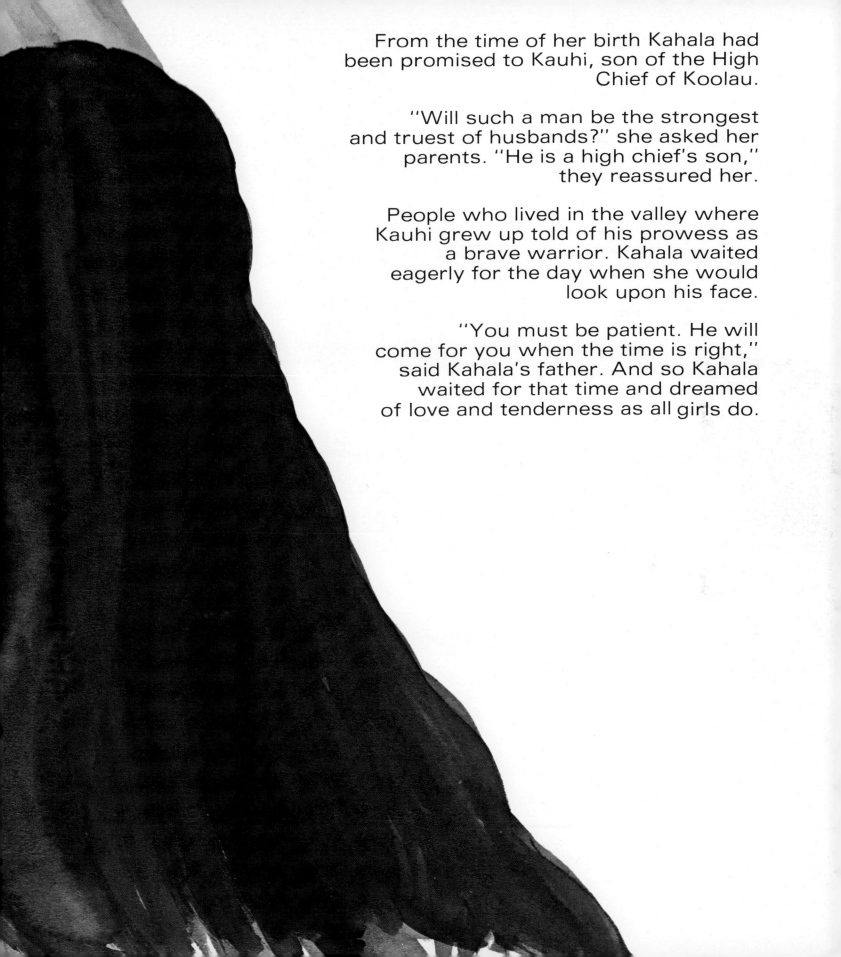

From the time of her birth Kahala had been promised to Kauhi, son of the High Chief of Koolau.

"Will such a man be the strongest and truest of husbands?" she asked her parents. "He is a high chief's son," they reassured her.

People who lived in the valley where Kauhi grew up told of his prowess as a brave warrior. Kahala waited eagerly for the day when she would look upon his face.

"You must be patient. He will come for you when the time is right," said Kahala's father. And so Kahala waited for that time and dreamed of love and tenderness as all girls do.

And in his valley, Kauhi also dreamed
his dreams of the beautiful girl of Manoa.
Once he came secretly to watch Kahala
from a distance.

Strong as he was in combat, Kauhi
found himself too shy to let Kahala
see him and too shy to try to speak
to her. So he returned to his dreams
where she walked to him down a
rainbow, clad in white tapa.

Kauhi yearned for the day of his
and Kahala's ho'ao, the day
they would be wed.

One day while fishing he overheard two of his friends talking.

"My heart still burns remembering that beauty in Manoa!" said one. "We were almost afraid to speak to her but she was so open and so friendly. She came up to us! The way she smiled—auwe!"

"Being with her is like being in the world of the gods!" said the second friend.

"A beautiful girl in Manoa?" asked Kauhi. "Which one?"

"Kahala!" they said. "You of all people should know her!" And they laughed.

Kauhi began to brood about their laughter and what they had told him. Jealous thoughts flooded his mind. Friendly? Smiling? Open? She came up to them? His Kahala, who in his dreams spoke only to him?

His black brooding thoughts grew until the pain inside him mounted to rage.

She must be punished! She was promised to me alone!

Kauhi hurried to Manoa and ran up the path into the valley. He tore off a heavy branch of the hala tree for a club.

From place to place he rushed, searching for Kahala.

At last, high in the valley, Kauhi heard the excited chatter of birds.

There, in a secluded pool at the base of a waterfall, Kahala bathed.

Birds circled near her.

Fish jumped and played around her.

Kauhi stood spellbound at the sight.

Tears came to his eyes. For an instant he wanted to rush to Kahala to tell her how he loved her.

His hand trembled but the weight of the hala branch reminded him. She had been open and smiled and talked to his friends! She who in his dreams had spoken only to him! She must be punished.

Kauhi stepped into the open where she could see him. "Kahala-o-Puna!" he called.

Quickly she covered herself with her kikepa.

She walked towards him, her gentle eyes questioning.

"I am Kauhi, you husband to be," he said sternly.
His voice and the expression on his face were not those of love.

Kahala gazed at him wondering why his eyes avoided hers. She wondered why she should feel such fear when she had waited so long for this moment.

"Follow me!" Kauhi commanded.

At the top of a hill Kauhi ordered her to kneel. "Do not look at me. I must not see your beauty or I will grow weak!"

Obedient, but more frightened than ever, Kahala knelt and turned away from him.

Kauhi raised the puhala club. It fell in one furious blow.

In the twilight Kauhi dug Kahala's grave with his bare hands and a rock. He covered her body with a mass of dry leaves.

Pueo had been watching. As soon as Kauhi left, the great blonde owl flew down. With his strong wings he brushed the leaves aside.

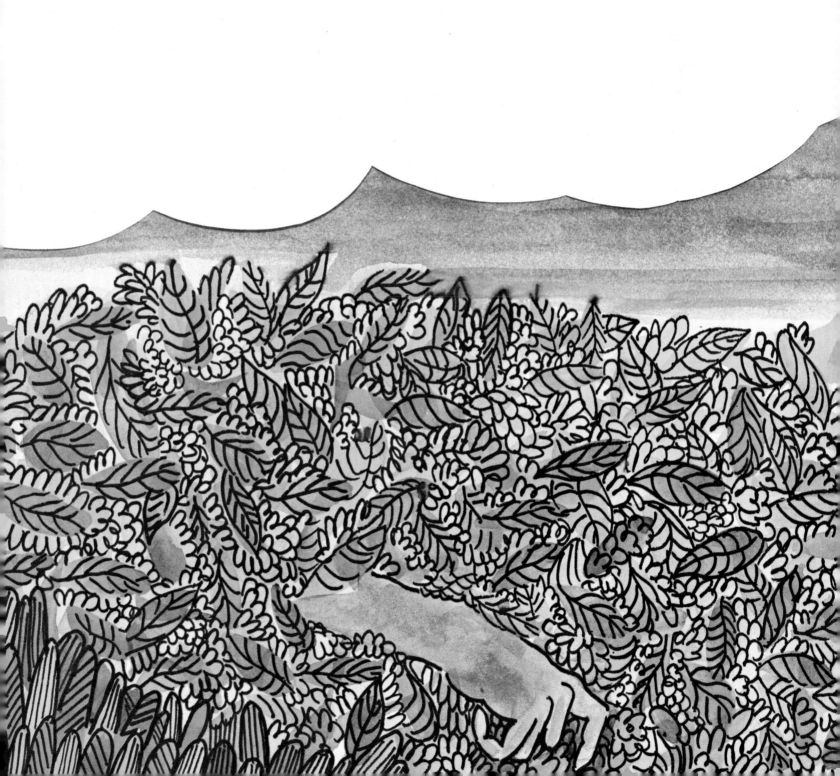

Gently Pueo gripped Kahala's body.
He carried her deep into the heart of
the Koolau Mountains, to a place known
only to creatures who fly.

The owls of Manoa brought la'au, the healing herbs, laukahi, the cool green leaves of ti and the strong smelling olapalapa with its life magic, ola. This powerful medicine was lovingly given to Kahala.

"When the sun rises, she will live again!" Pueo said.

All night the owls kept their vigil over her.

At sunrise Kahala stirred. She opened her eyes. Pueo had not left her side.

"Weeping, she told the great owl what had happened. "All my life, Pueo, I have had love for every living thing— and they all returned this love. All my life I have asked about Kauhi and dreamed of what his love might be."

As she talked, the bright mist of a rainbow touched her. "Pueo!" she asked. "How can I help Kauhi understand? How can I convince him that I have done no wrong?"

"Find him!" said Pueo. "Tell him what you have told me."

Kahala followed Pueo's advice and returned to the valley. She searched everywhere for Kauhi. In her hand she carried a pouch of hinano, the hala blossom with its power of love.

When she found him, Kauhi would not listen. The ugly tattoo of suspicion in his mind left his ears deaf, his eyes blind, his heart cold.

Again he took her to the mountaintop.

Once more the frightened Kahala knelt down before the angry Kauhi.

Again he raised the heavy club.

Again the sky turned red.

Again a chill wind blew.

Six times this happened. Six times Pueo saved her.

The seventh time Kauhi led her to a distant ridge in the Koolaus. This time he put her limp body under the roots of an Ohia tree. Then he covered her with huge rocks.

All that night Pueo and the owls of Manoa tried to pull the heavy rocks away. They could not. The sun rose and found them hunched in despair around Kahala's grave.

The morning showers blew down and with them came the rainbows. One arched up from the valley and ended on the rocks beneath which Kahala lay.

Up along the rainbow flew Elepaio, a small brown bird. He listened carefully to the sad story Pueo had to tell.

"I will help Kahala!" Elepaio offered. "You? How can you help her? You are smaller and weaker by far than we," said Pueo mournfully.

"I have Ike Pono, the magic gift of vision," said Elepaio. "I can see into the hearts and minds of men. Even now, in the valley, I see someone who can save Kahala!" And as quickly as he had appeared, the little bird flew away.

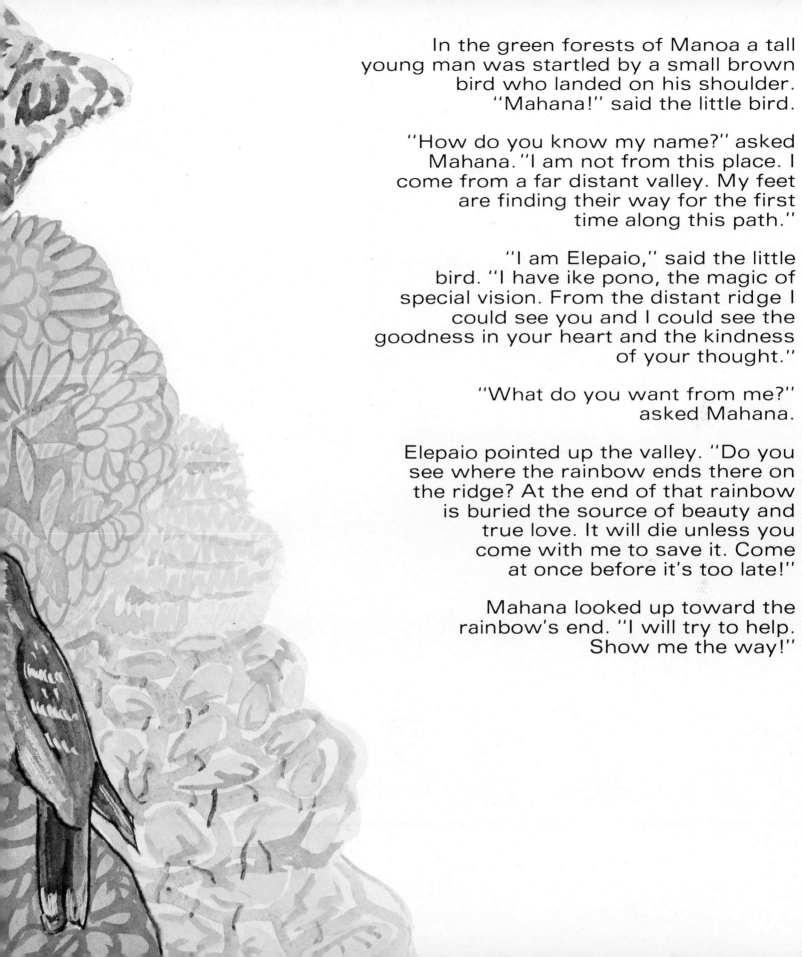

In the green forests of Manoa a tall young man was startled by a small brown bird who landed on his shoulder. "Mahana!" said the little bird.

"How do you know my name?" asked Mahana. "I am not from this place. I come from a far distant valley. My feet are finding their way for the first time along this path."

"I am Elepaio," said the little bird. "I have ike pono, the magic of special vision. From the distant ridge I could see you and I could see the goodness in your heart and the kindness of your thought."

"What do you want from me?" asked Mahana.

Elepaio pointed up the valley. "Do you see where the rainbow ends there on the ridge? At the end of that rainbow is buried the source of beauty and true love. It will die unless you come with me to save it. Come at once before it's too late!"

Mahana looked up toward the rainbow's end. "I will try to help. Show me the way!"

Mahana hesitated only a moment when he saw the huge boulders. Then, with muscles straining, he removed the great rocks one by one.

"She is so beautiful," he whispered when the last rock was removed. "Can we save her, little bird!"

"Yes, we have reached her in time," answered Elepaio, and they watched as the great owl worked with his healing herbs.

Mahana bent tenderly to lift her. He looked into Kahala's eyes and she into his. Their thoughts were filled with love. *Ua uhi 'ia ko la ua au manao i ke aloha.*

"So shall it be!" said Kahala's father.

"Mahana, you will build a house for our daughter here in Manoa. There you can love and protect her forever. When the house is ready that will be the day for your ho'ao!"

The night of the day called Huna, the eleventh night of the month, was set for the wedding. Not until then did Kauhi show himself in Manoa Valley. But on that night he appeared - uninvited, bold, without shame.

"This woman you would take as yours is 'uhane, a spirit, not a real person!" Kauhi charged.

"You lie!" Mahana grew angry.

"Lie? I am a high chief's son. I speak the truth! Seven times I killed her. I will stake my life against yours on what I say!"

"*He akua 'ai kahu ka holoholo olelo*," said the high chief sternly. "Gossip is a spirit that destroys its keeper, my son. If you speak the truth and Kahala is a ghost woman, then she will be put to the fire and Mahana with her. But if you are lying, my son, then it is you who must die! We will let the kahuna decide."

All the kahuna from Waianae to Leahi were called. Long into the night they discussed the matter in Manoa's largest temple.

All of them knew what had happened between Kahala and Kauhi. If in truth she were a ghost woman, then was not Kauhi to blame for this, some asked? Others were fearful of angering the high chief by doubting the word of his son.

After much argument the kahuna decided in favor of Kauhi. Just as they were ready to announce their decision they were startled by an eerie sound.

They ran out to see the night sky
filled with hundreds of owls. "Pueo! Pueo is
the guardian of Kahala and her family!" the kahuna cried.

"Our decision must be wrong!
We will change it. Better to risk
the anger of the high chief than the wrath of the gods."

"Kauhi lies! He must die."

So it was Kauhi, the high chief's son, who died in the fire in the first pale light before dawn.

At that instant, fishermen on the beach witnessed a strange sight. A shark, marked with Kauhi's cold eyes and fierce bearing, appeared in the first break of waves and then swam out to sea.

Like that shark, the memory of Kauhi soon vanished from
the thoughts of everyone in Manoa Valley.

From the night of their ho'ao, Mahana and Kahala
lived a life of sharing and joy.

Their house was a lively place, filled with
friends and relatives and strangers whom
they befriended.

Together, in all the openess of their love, Kahala
and Mahana roamed the valley, the beaches, the mountain
ridges with Pueo and Elepaio never far away.

Children were born to them. Years of happiness,
of loving and giving, adorned their lives.

One day, Kahala went swimming in the ocean and did not return. Mahana was frantic. He searched the water and the beaches but could not find his beloved Kahala. On the third day he found her shell wristlet at the water's edge. Kauhi had claimed her!

It was then that Mahana lost all hope. He knew he would never see her again. No one could save her now - not even Elepaio or Pueo.

For a long time, Mahana sat on the beach, grieving and despondent, feeling like an empty shell lost in the sand. He lifted his eyes to the high ridge of the Koolaus, to the bright span of the rainbows. It was there, long ago he had found Kahala, his source of beauty and true love.

Like a man possessed Mahana rose and ran toward the mountains. He did not notice that Elepaio had followed him.

On the distant ridge where the ohia tree still stood, Mahana fell on his hands and knees and began digging. With unbelievable strength, he hurled the giant rocks aside, but Kahala was not there. His tears soaked into the earth.

Exhausted, Mahana sank into the hole he had dug. Dry leaves fell and half covered his body. Without Kahala, he no longer wished to live.

A familiar voice roused him.

"Mahana!" The little brown bird, Elepaio, flew to his knee. "You grieve because Kahala is lost to you. But that does not mean Kahala's love is gone. That love which you found here at the rainbow's end is still alive inside you, Mahana. Don't you still feel that love very deeply?"

Mahana nodded, weeping.

"You must accept what has happened," said Elepaio. "You must go on living as you and Kahala always have. You must share love with all who will accept it until - as is the way of all things - your time will come to die.

"Do not be like Kauhi who believed that the source of true love was for him alone. Return to your valley, Mahana. Share with those who have not yet found love. Give it as Kahala did to all living things!"

Mahana rose and shook off the leaves. He felt the bright mist of the rainbow envelope him. He looked out over the peacefulness of the folded valleys.

"Yes, Elepaio, little bird, I understand."

To this day Manoa is still a valley of great beauty. When it rains there, the old Hawaiians tell their grandchildren, "Those bright Manoa showers are the tears of the gods. They are tears shed for Kahala-o-Puna, the beautiful maiden of Manoa, who knew and shared the spirit of Aloha, of love, with every living thing."

For a free complete catalog of
Island Heritage books, write to:
Island Heritage Limited
828 Fort Street Mall
Suite 400
Honolulu, Hawaii 96813